Sight-Singing 1

Déchiffrage pour le chant 1
Vom-Blatt-Singen 1

A fresh approach/Nouvelle approche
Eine erfrischend neue Methode

John Kember

SCHOTT

Mainz · London · Madrid · New York · Paris · Tokyo · Toronto

ED 12737
ISMN M-2201-2212-5

We wish to thank Blackheath Conservatoire of Music, London, Tim Jones,
Ben Odom, Hannah O'Hora, Jean Reynolds and Simon Tatnall for their valued
support, advice and encouragement in the preparation of this book.

ED 12737

British Library Cataloguing-in-Publication Data.
A catalogue record for this book is available from the British Library.
ISMN M-2201-2212-5

Design by www.adamhaystudio.com
Music setting by Woodrow
Printed in Germany S&Co.7555

Preface

The aim of this first sight-singing volume is to instill confidence in singers and to present a method of approaching all aspects of singing at sight.

Preparation:
The main rhythmic patterns of each example are presented along with the key and range of notes employed. Tonic and dominant notes are identified and semitones marked to help establish tonality.

Teachers are encouraged to create their own preliminary exercises to establish pulse and rhythms, tonality and intervals before a piece is attempted. In pieces where the accompaniment has a countermelody higher than the vocal line, it may be advantageous to omit this on the initial attempt and to re-instate it when the vocal line is established.

Many of the melodies follow familiar shapes and rhythms, and use sequences to aid recognition of these patterns. Singers are encouraged to observe how to obtain their starting note from the introduction and to note the help with their vocal line that can be found in the accompaniment.

Préface

L'objectif de ce premier recueil de déchiffrage pour le chant est de consolider la confiance en soi des chanteurs et d'offrir une méthode d'approche de tous les aspects du déchiffrage chanté.

Préparation :
Les principales formules rythmiques de chaque exemple sont présentées avec la tonalité et la tessiture des notes employées. Les toniques et les dominantes sont précisées et les demi-tons signalés afin d'aider à établir la tonalité.

Les maîtres sont invités à inventer leurs propres exercices préliminaires pour installer pulsation et rythmes, tonalité et intervalles avant d'attaquer un morceau. Dans les pièces dont l'accompagnement présente une contre-mélodie plus aiguë que la ligne vocale, il conviendra peut-être de ne pas la jouer lors du premier déchiffrage et de la rétablir quand la ligne vocale sera sûre.

Nombre des mélodies suivent des contours et des rythmes familiers et utilisent des séquences qui aident à leur reconnaissance. Les chanteurs sont entraînés à trouver leur note de départ dans l'introduction et à détecter l'aide que peut apporter l'accompagnement à la ligne vocale.

Vorwort

Ziel dieses ersten Bandes „Vom-Blatt-Singen" ist es, Sängern mittels einer Methode, die alle Aspekte des Vom-Blatt-Singens berücksichtigt, Sicherheit zu vermitteln.

Vorbereitung:
Am Beginn eines jeden Beispiels werden der Hauptrhythmus, die Tonart und der Tonumfang angegeben. Tonika und Dominante sowie Halbtöne sind gekennzeichnet, damit die Tonart leichter ermittelt werden kann.

Die Lehrer werden dazu ermuntert, ihre eigenen vorbereitenden Übungen zu entwickeln, um Rhythmen, Tonarten und Intervalle einzustudieren, bevor man das erste Stück in Angriff nimmt. Wenn die Begleitung eines Stückes eine Gegenstimme hat, die höher als die Gesangsstimme liegt, kann es vorteilhaft sein, diese am Anfang wegzulassen und sie erst hinzuzunehmen, wenn die Gesangslinie sicher beherrscht wird. Viele Melodien bestehen aus bekannten Formen und Rhythmen und verwenden Tonfolgen, die zur Wiedererkennung dieser Muster dienen. Den Sängern werden Möglichkeiten aufgezeigt, wie sie ihre Anfangsnote aus der Einleitung ableiten und ihre Gesangsstimme mit Hilfe der Begleitung finden können.

1.

Rhythms

Key: G major

2.

Rhythms

G major

3.

4.

5

6

5.

Rhythms

A minor

♩ = c.72

Am   Bm⁷⁻⁵/A   Am   Bm⁷⁻⁵/A   Am   Bm⁷⁻⁵/A

Am   E   Am   G   G#°   Am   E⁷

rall.   *a tempo*

F   Dm⁶   Em   F   Dm⁷   E⁹sus   E⁷   Am   Bm⁷⁻⁵/A   Am

6.

Rhythms

G major

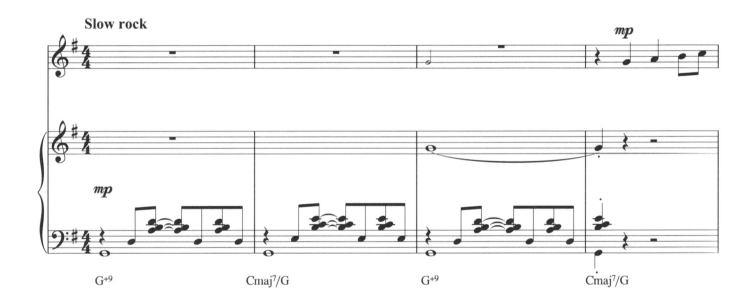

Slow rock

mp

mp

G+9   Cmaj7/G   G+9   Cmaj7/G

G+9   Cmaj7/G   G+9   Em7

7.

Rhythms

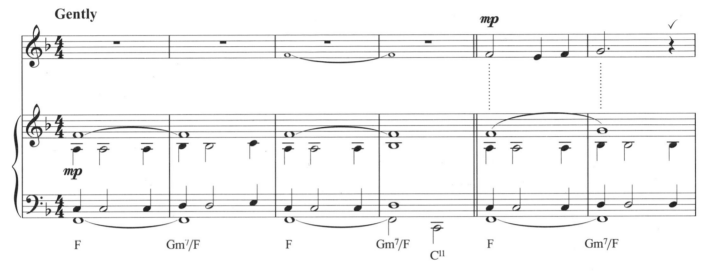

Gently

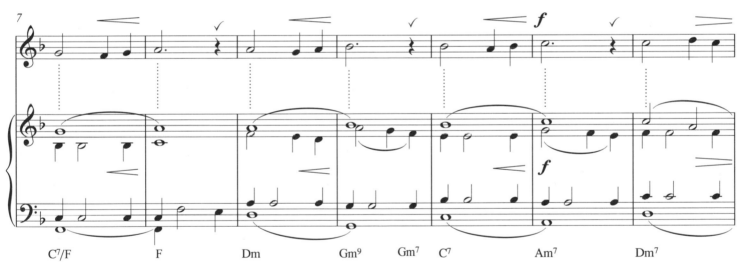

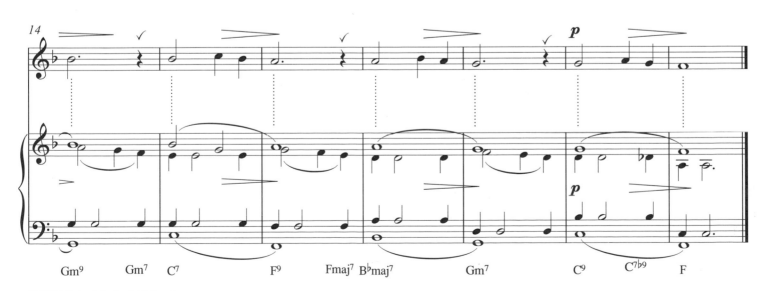

8.

Rhythms

F major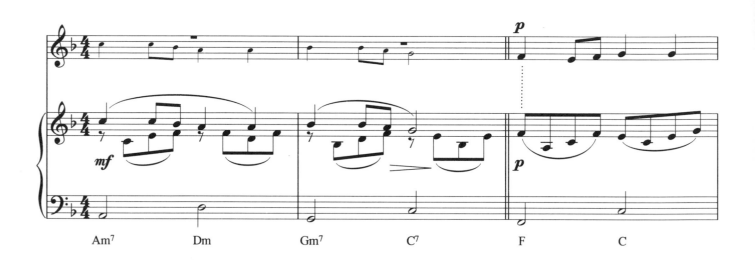

Am⁷   Dm   Gm⁷   C⁷   F   C

C⁷   F   Dm   Gm   C⁷   F

Am   Dm   Gm   C⁷   F   B♭   C⁷   F

9.

Rhythms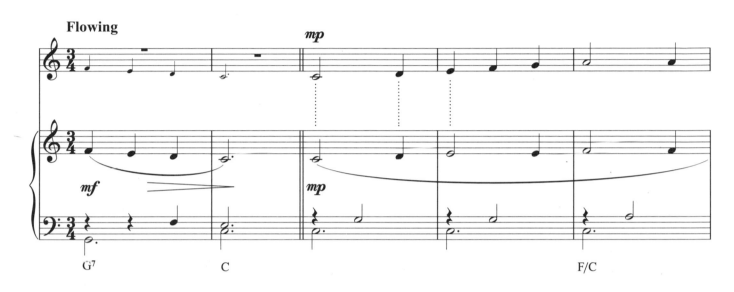

C major

Flowing

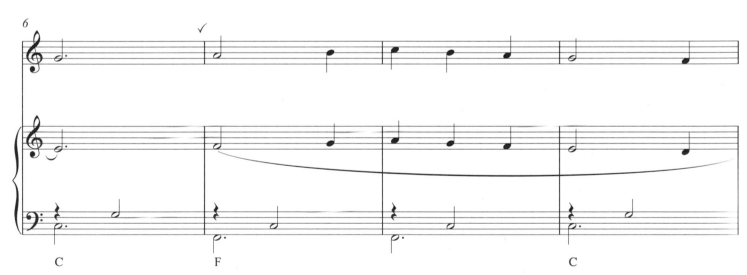

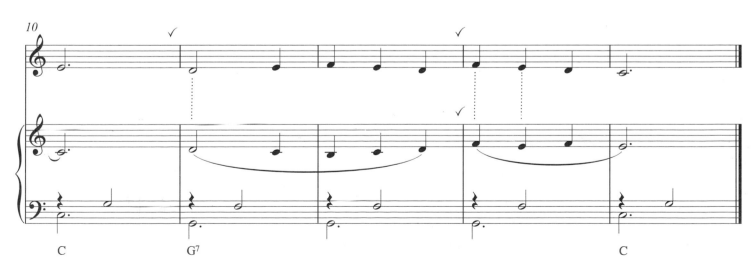

10.

Rhythms

F major

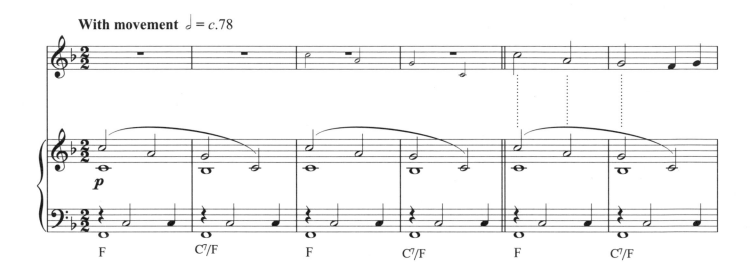

11.

Rhythms

F major

12.

Rhythms

13.

Rhythms

F major

14.

15.

Rhythms

F major

Not too fast ♩ = c.84

16.

Rhythms

G major

G+9   Em7   Am9   D7   Am7

D7   G   G7   C   Cm

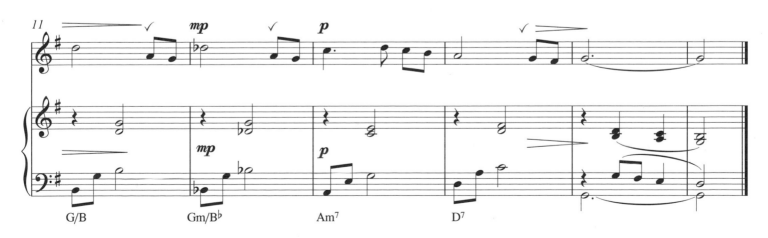

G/B   Gm/Bb   Am7   D7

17.

18.

Rhythms

D minor

19.

20.

21.

22.

23.

24.

Rhythms

E minor

Gentle 1-in-a-bar

Em   B⁷/E   Em

A⁷/E   Cmaj⁷   Bm⁹   Em   Em♯⁷

Am⁷   Em/B   B⁷   Em

25.

Key rhythms

F major

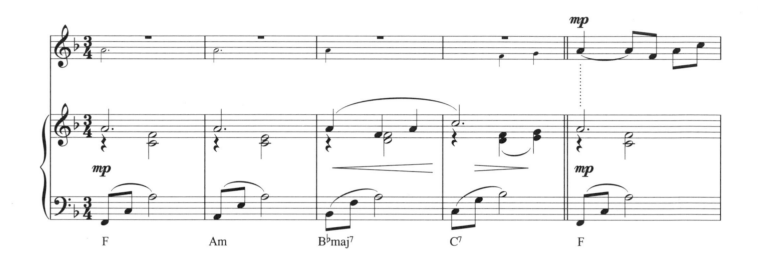

F   Am   B♭maj⁷   C⁷   F

Am   B♭maj⁷   C¹¹   Dm   Dm⁹⁽♯⁷⁾

Dm⁷   Am⁷   B♭maj⁷   C¹¹   F

26.

Rhythms

With a flowing movement

27.

28.

29.

Rhythms

A major

30.

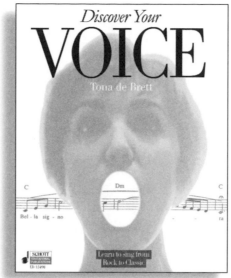

Voice Tutor & CD ED 12498
ISBN 0 946535 30 2

Discover Your Voice
(Tona de Brett)

Tona de Brett – internationally renowned singing teacher – presents
her teaching material, worked through with stars of rock, jazz and musicals
who seek help with their voices. Tona de Brett deals with the various aspects
of voice-production through a wealth of exercises and examples.

Discover Your Voice is aimed at all singers who take their voices seriously.

This book includes special exercises:
- Warming up
- Breathing technique
- Intonation
- Interpretation
- Articulation

Tona de Brett has taught, among others:
- Adam Ant
- Matt Bianco
- Tears for Fears
- Thompson Twins
- Annie Lennox Eurythmics)
- Vince Clark (Depeche Mode)
- Paul Hardcastle
- Tanita Tikaram
- Bananarama
- Richard Parfitt (Status Quo)
- Rick Astley
- Andy Summers (Police)
- Johnny Rotten (Sex Pistols)
- Seal
- Pauline Quirke, Linda Robson Jobs for the Girls
- Paul Young

Mainz · London · Madrid · New York · Paris · Tokyo · Toronto

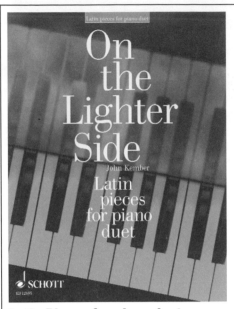

Latin Pieces for piano duet

7 Latin American style piano duets: Tango, Beguine, Samba, Bossa Nova, Salsa, Lambada and Rumba. These pieces are moderate to challenging in difficulty (Associated Board grades 4–6), and fun to play!
ED 12695

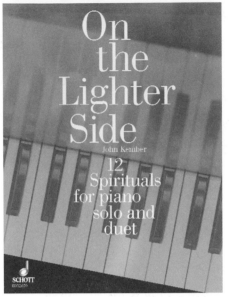

12 Spirituals for piano solo and duet arranged by John Kember

This collection consists of 7 solos and 5 duets including 'Steal Away', 'Swing Low, Sweet Chariot', 'Standing in Need of Prayer', 'Deep River', and 'Joshua Fight the Battle of Jericho'.
ED 12659

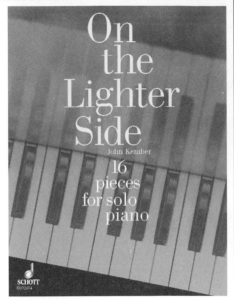

16 Pieces for Piano Solo

16 easy pieces in a variety of jazz-inspired styles including blues and swing. The standard of these pieces ranges from Associated Board grades 1–3, and they should prove useful initial preparation for examinations in jazz piano.
ED 12614

On the Lighter Side

A series of piano pieces by John Kember

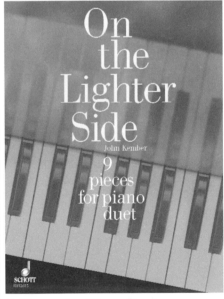

9 Pieces for Piano Duet

This collection provides an ideal introduction to playing in a variety of jazz-inspired styles: rock, latin, swing, ballad and ragtime. The teacher's part (secondo) provides the basic rhythm and 'groove', while the pupil (primo) has an easier, melodic part (grades 1–3).
ED 12615

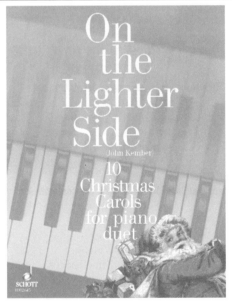

10 Christmas Carols for Piano Duet

Dual versions of 10 well-known Christmas carols. The initial versions are generally straightforward, while the second presents a more up-dated and sometimes up-tempo version to give variety and a fresh approach to some familiar tunes.
ED 12645

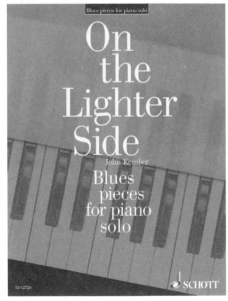

Blues Pieces for Piano Solo

14 original peices exploring the moods of the blues.
ED 12726

Send for a copy of the Schott Piano Music Catalogue
Website: www.schott-music.com

John Kember's website: www.johnkember.com

Mainz · London · Madrid · New York · Paris · Tokyo · Toronto